# The Manga Jesus
## Book One

GW00568232

## ABOUT THE AUTHOR

Siku – artist, theologian and musician – is one of Britain's leading comic book creators and conceptualists. He has worked for *2000AD*, on stories such as *'Judge Dredd'*, *'Slaine'* and a strip he co-created called *'Pan-African Judges'*. He has also worked for Marvel UK and COM X and has been credited on a number of computer games such as *Evil Genius*. More recently, he has been developing concept work for television commercials and producing freelance work for Nike, Nickelodeon IP, a BBC documentary-drama series and an animated television series.

Siku's works have been published in several books, including *Images 22: The Best of British Illustration* and *Digital Art Masters*. His work is prominent in Dez Skinn's *Comic Art Now* (a compilation of the best of international contemporary comic book art). His television appearances include ITV's *The London Programme,* Channel 4's *The Big Breakfast* and *More 4 News*, Channel 5's *Chris Moyles Show* and BBC One's *Heaven and Earth* show. He has also written editorials for magazines and industry books including *The Art of Game Worlds*.

Siku dreams of flying one day, just like Superman. Until then, he'll make do travelling around on the London Underground.

# The Manga Jesus
## Book One

### SIKU

HODDER & STOUGHTON

The Manga Jesus: Book One
Copyright © 2008 by Siku

First published in Great Britain in 2008 by Hodder & Stoughton
An Hachette Livre UK company

The right of Siku to be identified as the Author of the Work
has been asserted by him in accordance with the Copyright,
Designs and Patents Act 1988.

All rights reserved. No part of this publication may be reproduced,
stored in a retrieval system, or transmitted, in any form or by
any means, without the prior written permission of the publisher,
nor be otherwise circulated in any form of binding or cover
other than that in which it is published and without a similar
condition being imposed on the subsequent purchaser.

A CIP catalogue record for this title is available from the British Library

ISBN 978 0 340 96405 7

Printed and bound in Italy by Legoprint S.P.A.

Hodder & Stoughton policy is to use papers that are natural, renewable
and recyclable products and made from wood grown in sustainable
forests. The logging and manufacturing processes are expected to
conform to the environmental regulations of the country of origin.

Hodder & Stoughton Ltd
338 Euston Road
London NW1 3BH

www.hodderfaith.com

## ACKNOWLEDGEMENTS

Of all the books and films and songs about this man Yeshua, do we need another? I had audaciously accepted the task of doing yet another book about this most incredible of men, the man known to us as Jesus, and I think we have produced one of the most remarkable books on the subject. But without the team below, it would not have been so.

Thanks to Dr Conrad Gempf of the London School of Theology whose creative critique of my work makes the whole team look good. Rather than simply suggesting things to be cut out, you suggested things to be cut in. The London School of Theology has surprised me with the extent of its support and enthusiasm. I am humbled by this.

David Moloney, my editor, has been been with this project from the off. He had to believe I could make it work, he had to believe I had something unique to say about Yeshua of Nazareth.

My agent Ed Chatelier, of the Edge Group, cannot go without recognition. A man of vision and energy.

Then there is my wife, who is probably my greatest fan. Otherwise, how could she so patiently aid her workaholic of a husband?

As this book goes to press, I am concluding Book Two and developing ideas to accompany this great project of ours. There were times when I simply dreamed of plots and storylines, other times the parts were expressions of the trials and triumphs and failures, and the blood and tears in my life. That's what you see when you feel my guts in the drawings and the storytelling. But in it all, like a doting father tending to his young stumbling child, God was there. This is why my confession is bold: Yeshua of Nazareth is indeed the saviour and king of the universe!

Ding ding ding! Jesus... fiction... comic book... superhero. Alarm bells!

I'm a historian. My PhD thesis compared the work of St Luke with the best of the Greek and Roman historians. This project flashed twenty different kinds of red lights in my head.

OK, I knew Siku. He did an undergraduate degree in theology where I work, The London School of Theology, formerly known as London Bible College. He's a great student. I worked with him on the New Testament portion of The Manga Bible, which illustrates the text of Scripture in manga form. It is most excellent.

But this?! To fill in gaps that the Bible leaves blank?
To employ a medium we associate with ludicrous and outrageous fantasies to portray what I think is truth? Ding ding ding!

I was approached to be the 'theological consultant'. Ummm. Thought I'd have to say no. Decline gracefully. This might be going too far.

Then I saw the material. Whoa! He's done his homework! He knows the ancient sources; he's sensitive to the ancient culture. Whoa!

Then I saw the drawings. Wow! He's totally captured John the Baptist; his gap-filling is helpful rather than distracting. And, I'm sorry, for me that IS the Temple.

And then, beyond wow! This is not only filled with learning about the ancient world. It's also so clearly filled with sympathy for the characters and, better still, filled with love for the Scriptures and for the Lord.

You look at these pages — or through these pages — a man pushes the hood back from his head and turns to you. A wry smile. And with the suggestion of a twinkle in his eye, he says to you — to you — 'Oh. By the way... They call me Yeshua — Jesus.'

Gulp.

Yeah, ok, maybe manga comics seemed inappropriate. A worldly medium. An earthen vessel. Just like any of us.

No more alarms; sound the 'all clear'. For some people in today's culture — all very, very clear.

**Dr Conrad Gempf, London School of Theology**

I was to do 15 live radio interviews in two hours. All in one sitting, moving from one BBC breakfast show host to the next. As I sat alone in the BBC's local station in Essex, waiting to be cued in for the second interview, I thought to myself, 'Well, the first went well, now I've just got to find the same enthusiasm for the next 14!' As it turned out, the thirteenth was the last and this time I got be interviewed in the flesh by the BBC Essex radio hosts. They were particularly struck by my energy and passion and said they rarely got such enthusiasm from people talking about their faith! For me, it was just a welcome relief from being stuck all alone in a BBC studio furnished with those olive coloured carpets you see on 70s TV dramas like *Ironside* or *The Rockford Files*. The engineers cued me in through a device that studio people call 'talk back'. Actually, it's a sort of intercom that feeds through the headphone. You talk back through your microphone. That week, I did 20 interviews to promote *The Manga Bible*.

By now, the publicity machine had cranked into full gear. My brother and collaborator, Akin, and I had finished the New Testament books and we were approaching the finish line of the Old Testament. The interview requests were coming in from all over the world – Mexico, Brazil, Australia – and then I got a surprise request from an old friend of mine, George Luke, who interviewed me in my publisher's offices at Euston in London. We just about got something loosely resembling an interview for all the laughing and kidding around we did. He learned an important principle that day – 'Never interview a friend'. I had done over 40 assorted interviews, from cable TV to terrestrial TV, print and web media! We cranked out 30 pages of artwork in one week – the titles of our blogs said it all: 'Attack of the Killer Deadlines' (27/02/2007) and then, 'Mission Impossible' (03/03/2007). You might be forgiven for thinking I was going nuts with the title, 'Ever tried an escape route through sewage?' (03/03/2007), and then there was, 'Oops, there it is!' (10/06/2007). No, that title was unrelated to the previous heading

– we had just delivered final corrections for the Old Testament. *The Manga Bible* was now complete! But then the road show began, and so unto Telford in the English Midlands for a booksellers' conference with press, radio, conference interviews and hundreds of books to be signed. It was the Thursday evening of that week, still buzzing from success at Telford, when my body simply packed up. For every action, there is an equal and opposite reaction. This was mine coming home to roost and it was time for me to rest and take stock.

For all the plaudits for *The Manga Bible*, I felt there was unfinished business. The complete book was only 200 pages long, of which we devoted only one page to the book of Job, four pages to Revelation, and 30 pages to Jesus. Keeping it short and accessible was our way of getting the Bible into the hands of the lad and lady on the street. But we wanted to show you what we could really do. How about going tenfold on Jesus for starters? So my publishers and I decided to produce a 300-page epic on Jesus, split into three books of 100 pages each. For me, this was the noblest of tasks. Of all the heroes in all genres – from film noir to sci-fi, from romance to fantasy epics, in every culture and civilisation – if I had to do a book on one hero's life, it would be that of Jesus Christ.

We started work in December 2007. I started my research in the theological school's library, where my old principal Dr Derek Tidball found me and quipped that he had seen more of me as a graduate than through my three years of learning. By this point, we had agreed to set Jesus in his historical environment. Previously, we wanted to set him in space! I had put together a three-part story running across three different genres, one of them being space opera (like *Star Wars*).

Don't laugh! If done well, it could work! My editor and I are what you might call 'fanboys' – you know: 'geeks', 'sci-fi nerds', etc – so for us, it made sense. But in the end we agreed (after a little arm-twisting from Hodder's MD) that it was too much of a leap from *The Manga Bible*. In other words, cooler heads prevailed!

The next problem was one that we had also encountered in *The Manga Bible* – how to harmonise the four gospel accounts of the Bible into one single narrative. This had been one of the hardest tasks of *the Manga Bible* although, with only 30 pages to tell Jesus' story, we got away with solving very few questions. But now, with a 300-page epic in front of us, the task was more ominous. I also had the challenge of trying to fill in some of the historical gaps left by the writers of the gospels. This was important, to create a stronger and more credible gospel story.

I had to pick my way carefully through the accounts of historians both ancient and contemporary, many of which conflicted with each other and some of which – particularly the histories of the ancients – were over-excitable to say the least! Much of what I discovered and developed is present in the three volumes.

Placing the gospels within a historical context based on the latest research was a work long overdue in graphic novels. But – nutter that I am – I had to go one step further. I had to create an authentic 1st century context.

Context!

Do you remember those old Bible story films with 'thee' and 'thou' going 'forth'? They were designed to make us feel we were watching something authentic, whereas in actual fact, we were just watching white English-speaking men behaving like white English-speaking men roughly three hundred years ago! Those who criticised *The Manga Bible* for being too colloquial (being 'street') do not understand that in being so loose with language, we were aiming to create a more accurate picture of what the people of the time actually sounded like to each other. People were energetic and expressive and passionate.

So you'll forgive me for not allowing my characters in this new volume to behave like white English-speaking men. They are not polite characters from a Jane Austen story, struggling to contain their emotions until they all erupt. The Peter in this story is unrestrained. The tension within the group of twelve students of Jesus rapidly boils over into open conflict. Jesus' passion for God is unbridled. Galilee sizzles with revolutionary fervour and John the Baptist does his best to see just how insulting he can be without sinning.

But *The Manga Jesus* isn't just about explosive arguments. Much of first-century life looks like our own. Like the house and land repossessions that occurred at that time. The development of cash crops meant people could not afford food. Just as we face inflationary prices due (in part) to land being used to farm products for bio-fuels, they faced the use of land used to grow cash crops such as cotton instead of food. Countless numbers suffering from leprosy, blindness, disability and other illnesses is not something exclusive to the peoples of the ancient world. They exist in our world too.

These are the people you will meet in this volume. Rough-necks, thieves and cut-throats, prostitutes and collaborators all heeding the call of the greatest person who ever lived.

I hope you enjoy Book One of *The Manga Jesus*.

**Siku**
**Essex, England, July 2008.**

"THEY SAY NOTHING GOOD COMES OUT OF GALILEE..."

# The Manga Jesus

## Prologue: Nothing good comes out of Galilee

FIVE WEEKS AGO: THE TEMPLE MOUNT, JERUSALEM.
NAME THEM MARTYRS!
MACCABEES!
WE WANT HEROD ARCHELAUS TO DECLARE THEM MARTYRS!
MACCABEES!
JUDAS AND MATTHIAS MACCABEES ARE HEROES NOT CRIMINALS!
THEY WERE FRIENDS OF GOD!
THEY DIDN'T DIE FOR NOTHIN
WE WANT THEM REMEMBERED!

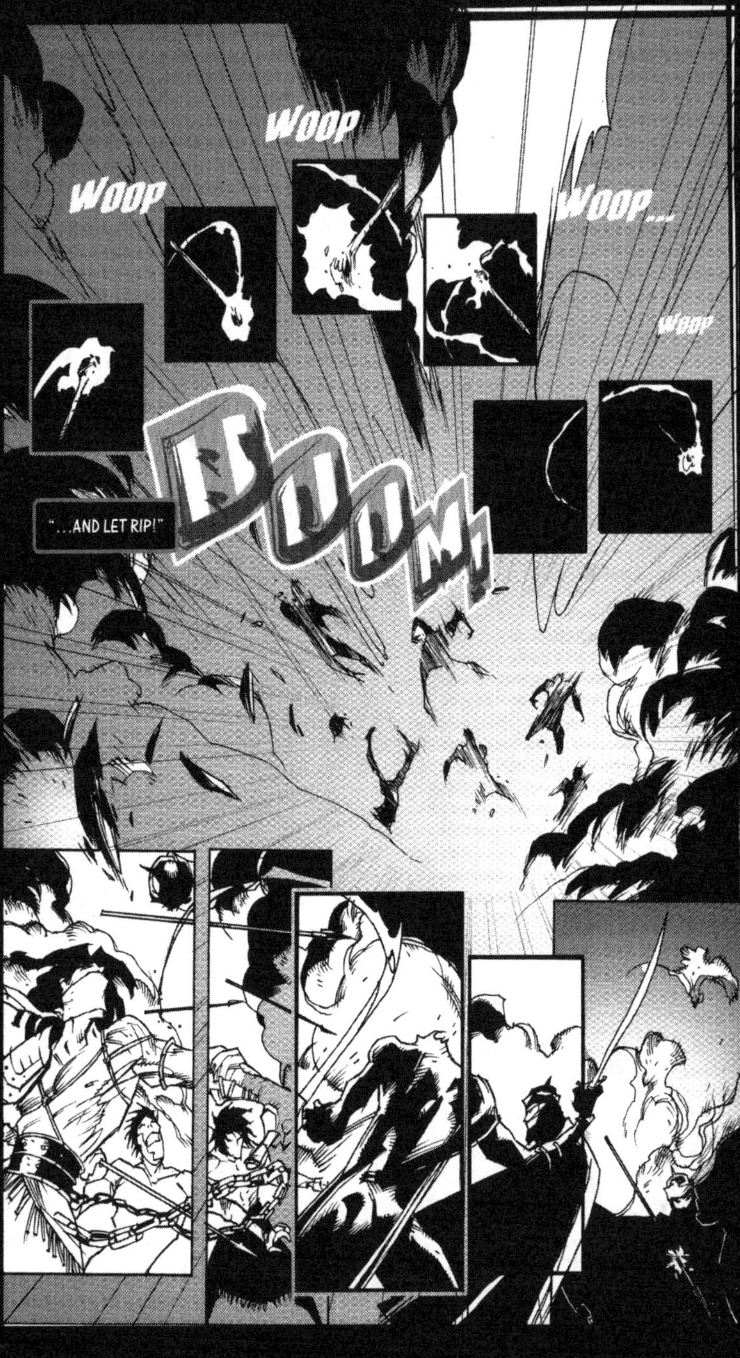
WOOP
WOOP
WOOP...
WOOP
"...AND LET RIP!"
BOOM!

"...INSTEAD WE HAVE HIS BROTHER, THAT NUTCASE, ARCHELAUS."

"WE CAN'T GO BACK HOME TO BETHLEHEM, SO INSTEAD WE GO NORTH TO GALILEE..."

"...THAT SEETHING HOTBED OF REVOLUTIONARIES AND **REVOLUTION**."

...

JOSEPH...

"OUR NEW HOME..."

"...NAZARETH."

"FOUR MILES FURTHER **SEPPHORIS** BURNS."

"WELCOME TO GALILEE!"

# Chapter 16
# Lost

THE
GREAT
SEA

TYRE

SYRO-PHOENICIA

CAESAREA
PHILIPPI

GALILEE

CHORAZIN    BETH-SAIDA
CAPERNAUM    GAMLA
MAGDALA
TIBERIAS    SEA
OF
GALILEE

BETHLEHEM

NAZARETH    GADARA

NAIN

MEGIDO    DECAPOLIS

SAMARIA

SHECHEM    SYCHAR
JACOB'S WELL

ARIMATHAEA    PERAEA

EMMAUS    JERICHO

JERUSALEM
BETHANY
BETHLEHEM
HERODIUM

JUDEA

HEBRON    MACHAERUS

DEAD
SEA

ARNON RIVER
GORGE

MASADA

ER-SHEBA

★ PLACES OF INTEREST

▸▸▸ YESHUA'S TRAVELS

'A GUY WANTED TO GET IN THE TEMPLE ON YOM KIPPUR, BUT WITHOUT A TICKET THEY DON'T LET HIM IN.'

'SO HE SAYS, "LISTEN PAL, I JUST WANT TO GIVE A MESSAGE TO A MATE IN THERE."'

SO WHAT DID THE GUY SAY NEXT?

HE REPLIES, "JUST LET ME IN FOR ONE SEC, THEN I'LL BE RIGHT OUT."

"OKAY....," SAYS THE GUY AT THE DOOR, "...BUT I BETTER NOT CATCH YOU PRAYING."

HAHA HA HA HA HA HAAAA!

YESHUA! DID YOU HEAR THAT?

YESHUA!

YESHUA'S NOT DOWN HERE UNCLE JOSEPH. I THOUGHT HE WAS WITH YOU.

YESHUA!

YESHUA!

YESHUA!

YESHUA!

YESHUA!

DAY TWO.

'GUYS, MARY AND I HAVE DECIDED TO CONTINUE OUR SEARCH IN JERUSALEM. WE'LL HEAD UP TO BETHANY FIRST.'

GO ON TO GALILEE WITHOUT US.

KNOCK
KNOCK

JOSEPH! MARY! IS SOMETHING WRONG?

IT'S YESHUA, MIRIAM. WE CAN'T FIND HIM ANYWHERE.

WE THOUGHT HE WAS WITH HIS OTHER SIBLINGS AND COUSINS. IF ANYTHING'S HAPPENED TO MY SON...

SHUSH NOW MISSY, I'M SURE HE'LL BE IN JERUSALEM WAITING FOR YOU.

IT'S BEEN TWO DAYS, CLEOPAS. TWO DAYS OUR SON HAS BEEN OUT THERE.

DAY THREE.
UUGGHHH!
GOOD MORNING JERUSALEM!
HELLO THERE SON. COME ON IN, THERE'S ROOM FOR ONE MORE.
NOW TODAY WE ARE GOING TO BRUSH UP ON OUR INTERPRETATION OF LAW.

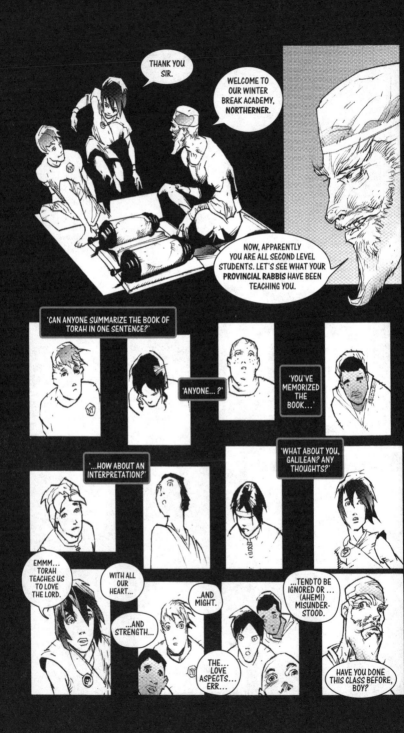

BETHANY.

WHO'S THE MAN, WHO'S THE MAN?

HA HA HAA HAAA!

TEE HEE!

JOHN THINKS BECAUSE HE'S DONE HIS BAR MITZVAH, HE'S THE MAN.

NOW THAT JOHN'S A MAN HE WON'T LET YESHUA LIVE IT DOWN FOR THE NEXT YEAR.

YEAH... A MAN AT THIRTEEN YEARS OF AGE...

BY THE WAY, HOW'S JOHN'S PRIESTHOOD TRAINING GOING?

HE'S DOING QUITE WELL, MARY. HE'S WELL PLACED TO TAKE HIS FATHER'S PLACE.

LOOK AT THEM... YOU'D NEVER KNOW HE'D BEEN LOST THREE DAYS. BOYS HUH? ESPECIALLY THOSE TWO...

THOSE TWO, CLEOPAS. TROUBLE.

# Chapter 3
# Filthy tax collectors, Romans and Herodians

THE GREAT SEA

TYRE

SYRO-PHOENICIA

CAESAREA PHILIPPI

GALILEE

CHORAZIN   BETH-SAIDA

CAPERNAUM   GAMLA

MAGDALA   SEA OF GALILEE

TIBERIAS

BETHLEHEM

NAZARETH   GADARA

NAIN

MEGIDO   DECAPOLIS

SAMARIA

SHECHEM   SYCHAR
JACOB'S WELL

ARIMATHAEA

PERAEA

EMMAUS   JERICHO

JERUSALEM   BETHANY
BETHLEHEM

JUDEA   HERODIUM

HEBRON   MACHAERUS

DEAD SEA   ARNON RIVER GORGE

MASADA

BEER-SHEBA

★ PLACES OF INTEREST

▸▸▸▸ YESHUA'S TRAVELS

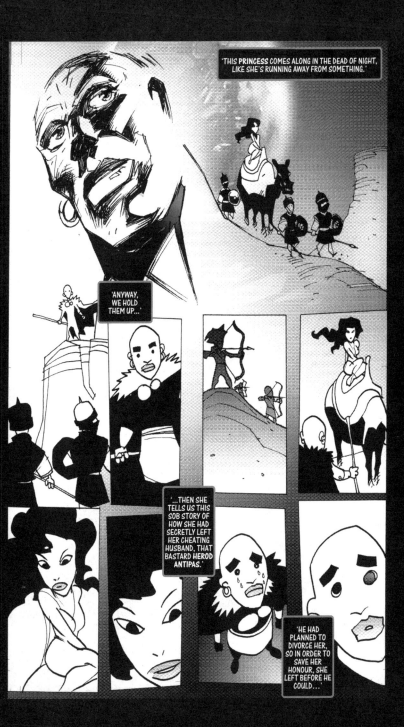

'NOW YOU REMEMBER MY STORY ABOUT THE PRINCESS?'

...SO I HELP THE WEE PRINCESS TO THE MACHAERUS FORT USING SECRET ROUTES. HER FATHER KING ARETAS OF NABATEA WOULD FETCH HER LATER.

'BUT I DIGRESS.'

'THAT SAME NIGHT THIS MACHO PROPHET GEEZER IN CAMEL SKIN LIVING IN THE DESERT WITH THEM BLASTED DEMONS COMES UP TO ME...'

'WHAT HE SAID TO ME THAT NIGHT HAS HAUNTED ME FOR EIGHT YEARS.'

'I HEAR HE'S BAPTIZING FOLKS AT BETHANY, EAST OF JORDAN RIVER.'

TOMORROW, WE ALL GET BAPTIZED!

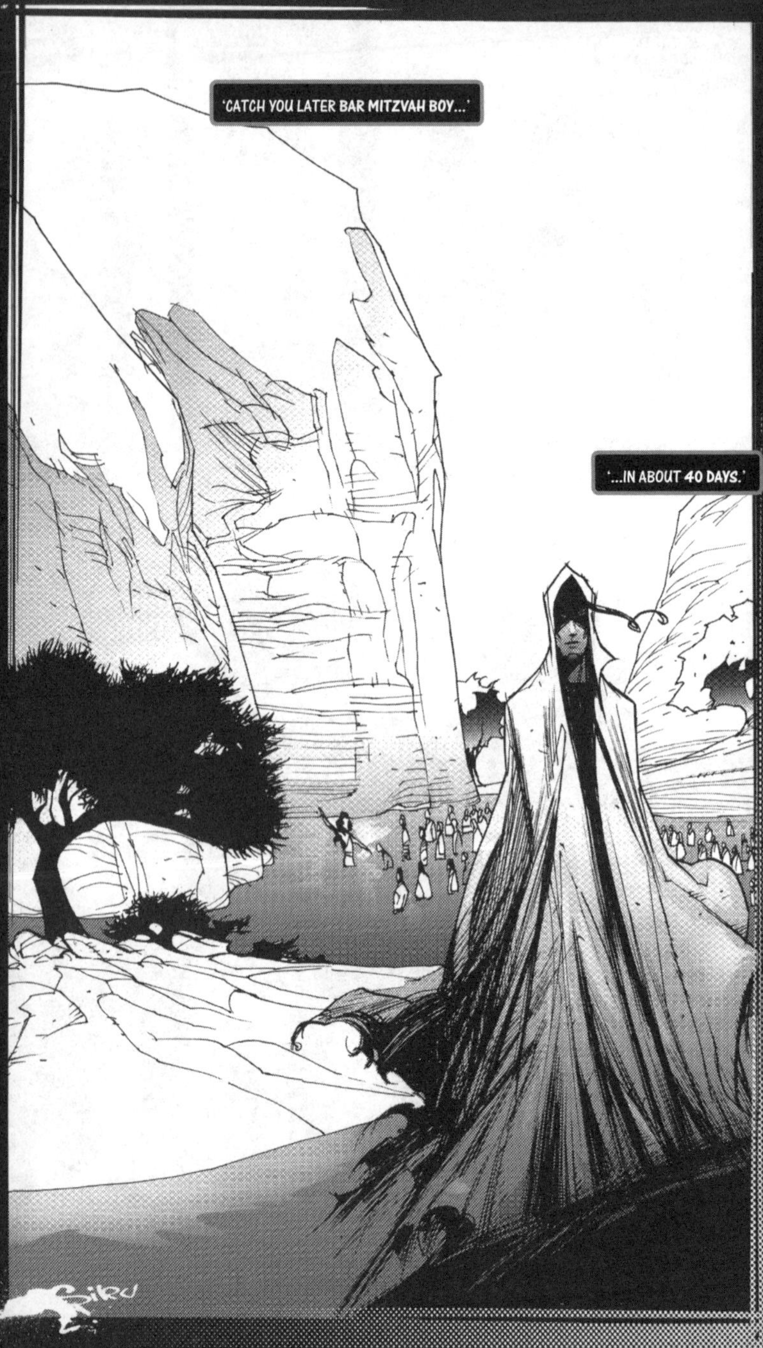
'CATCH YOU LATER BAR MITZVAH BOY...'
'...IN ABOUT 40 DAYS.'

# Chapter 3

# Can anything good come out of Nazareth?

THE GREAT SEA

TYRE

CAESAREA PHILIPPI

SYRO-PHOENICIA

GALILEE

CHORAZIN

BETH-SAIDA

CAPERNAUM

GAMLA

MAGDALA

TIBERIAS

SEA OF GALILEE

BETHLEHEM

NAZARETH

GADARA

NAIN

DECAPOLIS

MEGIDO

SAMARIA

SHECHEM

SYCHAR

JACOB'S WELL

ARIMATHAEA

PERAEA

EMMAUS

JERICHO

JERUSALEM

BETHANY

BETHLEHEM

HERODIUM

JUDEA

HEBRON

MACHAERUS

DEAD SEA

Arnon River Gorge

MASADA

ER-SHEBA

★ PLACES OF INTEREST

‹‹‹‹ YESHUA'S TRAVELS

MONDAY.

THE **TYROPOEAN VALLEY**, JERUSALEM.

HEROD'S HIPPODROME.

WHY DO THE NATIONS IMAGINE A VAIN THING...

THE RABBI'S PRAYING AGAIN.

STRANGE.

WHAT'S STRANGE?

HOW HE KEEPS CALLING GOD 'FATHER'.

KANA.

# Chapter 4
# A storm brews

THE
GREAT
SEA

TYRE

SYRO-PHOENICIA

CAESAREA
PHILIPPI

GALILEE

CHORAZIN • • BETH-SAIDA
CAPERNAUM • • GAMLA
MAGDALA •
TIBERIAS • SEA
OF
GALILEE

BETHLEHEM •
NAZARETH •
NAIN • GADARA

MEGIDO • DECAPOLIS

SAMARIA

SHECHEM • • SYCHAR
• JACOB'S WELL

PERAEA

ARIMATHAEA •

EMMAUS • • JERICHO

JERUSALEM ★ • BETHANY
BETHLEHEM •
JUDEA HERODIUM • ★

HEBRON • ★ MACHAERUS

DEAD
SEA
ARNON RIVER
GORGE

MASADA •

BEER-SHEBA •

★ PLACES OF INTEREST

⤏ YESHUA'S TRAVELS

NIGHTFALL AT THE TIBERIAS FORTRESS IN GALILEE.

HERODIAS.

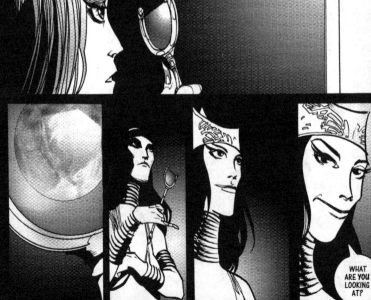

WHAT ARE YOU LOOKING AT?

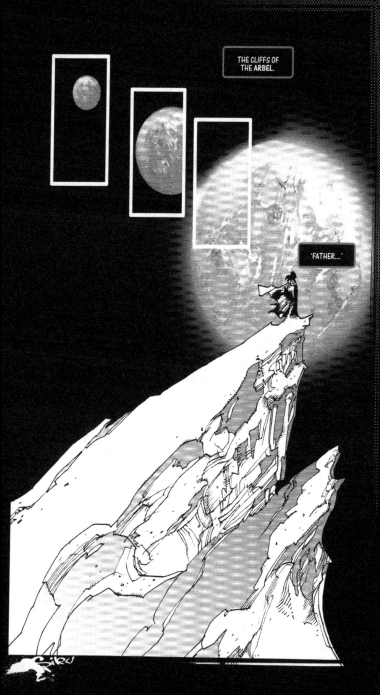

'MANY MOONS AGO, WHILE I WAS IN THE DESERT, YOU SUSTAINED ME.'
'THE YOUNG LIONS DO LACK, AND SUFFER HUNGER...'
'BUT THEY THAT SEEK THE LORD WILL NOT LACK ANY GOOD THING.'

'FATHER, YOU HAVE LAID ME INTO THE LOWEST PIT, IN DARKNESS...'

'IN THE DEEPS.'

'BUT EVEN IF THE DARKNESS SHOULD ENGULF ME...'

'THE DARKNESS IS NOT DARK FOR YOU.'

'NIGHT IS AS DAY FOR YOU, FATHER.'

'FOR THE ENEMY HUNTS ME AS I DWELL IN DARKNESS...'

'...LIKE THOSE LONG DEAD.'

snarl

'I WILL NOT FEAR...'

'...THE TERROR OF THE NIGHT.'

THE CONTUBERNIA!

WHAT DO THE CONTUBERNIA WANT WITH US?

GET THE WOMEN AND KIDS INTO THE CELLARS!

OH PIOUS DESERT DWELLERS! TELL US WHERE THE BAPTIST IS AND NO HARM WILL COME TO YOU!

MEN! GET IN THERE! LET'S LOOSEN THOSE PIOUS TONGUES!

'The LORD doth build up
Jerusalem...

PASSOVER.
If I do not remember thee, let my tongue cleave to the roof of my mouth; if I prefer not Jerusalem above my chief joy.
Because of thy temple at Jerusalem...
...shall kings bring presents unto thee.

NOW FOR SOMETHING A LITTLE HARDER..
HOW ABOUT THE NEXT TIME HEROD COMMANDS YOU TO ARREST AN INNOCENT MAN, YOU JUST TELL HIM TO GO SUCK A LEMON?
ONE MOUTHY PRISONER DELIVERED. THEY CALL HIM THE-VOICE.
THEY GOT THAT RIGHT... HE'S GIVEN ME ONE BLOOMINGHEAD-ACHE!
HEH HEH HEH,DON'T WORRY, VOICE. WE'LL SOON TURN THAT VOICE INTO A YELP!
HAAAAH!

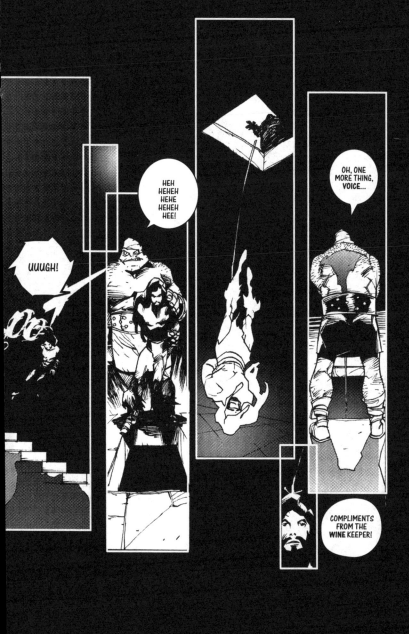

These next few pages show the development of characters, storyboards and layouts.

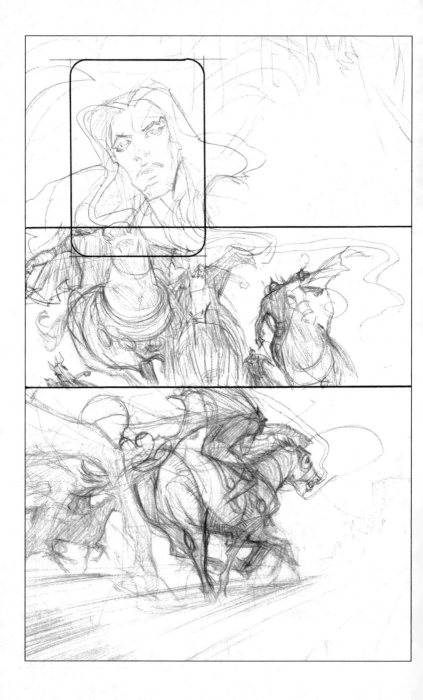

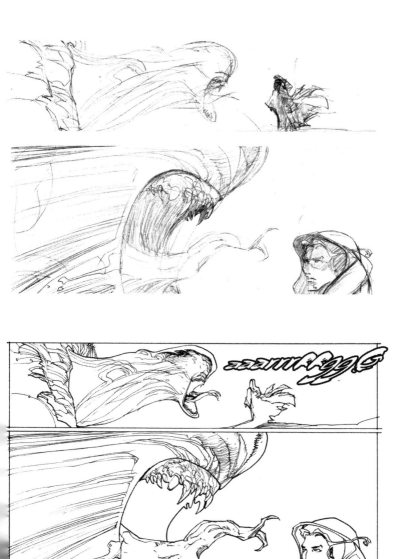

**Abraham**
The father of the Hebrews. Christians claim him as their spiritual father.

**Baptism**
A purification rite prescribed by Hebrew law, required for certain rites and conversion. John introduced a radical form of baptism which announced impending judgement and the coming kingdom.

**Bar Mitzvah**
A ritual ceremony marking the 13th year of boyhood, after which the child takes responsibility for their own moral and spiritual conduct and is thereafter considered adult. Today, the similar ceremony for girls is called a Bat Mitzvah.

**Caiaphas**
High priest and chairman of the Sanhedrin between 18 AD and 37 AD.

**Chanuth, the**
The market place on the Mount of Olives, across the Kidron valley from the Temple.

**Christ, the**
From the Greek, literally meaning 'the Anointed'. Its Hebrew origin is 'the Messiah'. In the Old Testament the title implied little more than 'set apart to perform a particular task'.

**Contubernia, the**
Otherwise called 'the tent group'. Comprising eight legionaries, it was the smallest organised unit in the Roman army.

**Demon possession**
When demons lay claim to and reside within a human's body and personality, such is said to be possessed.

**Elijah**
Considered one of the greatest of the prophets, Elijah lived in the ninth century BC. Jews expect his return as a precursor to the coming of the Messiah.

**Ethnarch**
A ruler of an ethnic group as designated by Roman power. While this office is higher than the title tetrarch, it is not quite as high as the King. An example of an ethnarch who sought the higher office of king within the Roman Empire was Herod Archelaus, who ruled over Samaria, Judea and Idumea.

**Galilee**
The largest and furthest north of the three provinces (with Judea and Samaria) that comprised Israel in Roman times. It also was the most troublesome politically.

**Gentiles**
Non-Jews and non-followers of the Jewish faith.

### Herod
Name used of the kings and rulers in the centuries just before and after Jesus, descended from Herod the Great (and his father Antipater).

### Herod the Great
Otherwise known as Herod the Builder, born 73 BC, died 4 BC. Brutal and paranoid Client King of Judea and father of Archelaus, Antipas and Philip. He was famous for his many great buildings including the second temple in Jerusalem. His infamous slaughter of the Bethlehem babies and toddlers in his hunt for Yeshua is well known.

### Jerusalem
The sacred capital of Israel and the Jewish faith. The seat of the temple of God.

### Jews
Descendants of Abraham.

### Maccabees
An epitaph meaning 'the hammer', and the name of a Jewish liberation movement. Inspired by the high priest Mattathias, his sons – Judas Maccabee and his brothers – led a successful revolt against the Seleucid Empire.

### Passover
A Jewish festival celebrating Israel's exodus from slavery in Egypt. It is performed in spring time.

### Pharisees
An old Jewish sect that promoted a constant state of purity, which they believed would ensure the survival of the nation of Israel. They obeyed both the oral and written law (Torah).

### Prophet
An inspired teacher, known at times to predict the future. Sometimes described as a seer.

### Rabbi
Literally means 'my great one'. A teacher and master of Jewish religious law. Only the most distinguished students qualify to study to the level of Rabbi.

### Sadducees
A priestly, aristocratic caste. They were traditionalists who accepted only the written law as inspired scripture and rejected belief in the afterlife.

### Sanhedrin
The Jewish high council made up of 71 members, both Pharisees and Sadducees. A high priest presided over the council.

### Synagogues
Places of worship, religious instruction, education and community in first century AD Israel.

### Synagogue interpreter (Amora)
The Hebrew scriptures were written in Hebrew and as such needed

interpretation (Aramaic being the common language of first century Palestine) by an Amora, who would interpret as the reader read from the scriptures. Sometimes, the Amora commented on difficult verses.

### Social bandits
Revolutionaries who ravaged the countryside and toll routes. They usually saw themselves as rebels against Roman tyranny and often supported society's poor and outcasts.

### Temple, the
The Temple was the national centre of worship for the Hebrews. It was the seat of the presence of God on earth. The magnificent Temple of Solomon had been destroyed in 587 BC by Babylonian power, but rebuilt during the reign of Cyrus (538 BC). By 19 BC, Herod the Great had begun rebuilding the Temple, restoring it to its former magnificence.

### Tetrarch
Four tetrarchs would lead an ethnic group or province in the first century BC Near East, within the Roman Empire. All tetrarchs were subordinate to an ethnarch.

### Tiberius, Emperor
Known as Tiberius Caesar Augustus or Tiberius I, he reigned as tyrannical Roman Emperor from 14 AD to 37 AD after a distinguished military career.

### Torah, the
The written law, otherwise known as the Mosaic law. The first five books of the Hebrew bible comprise the Torah. It is distinct from the oral law, which is called the Mishnah.

### Yeshua
The original Aramaic proper name for Jesus. A common name during the era of the second Temple, it is translated 'salvation'.

### Yom Kippur
This is the holiest day of the Jewish year, the Day of Atonement, and is usually celebrated with a 24-hour period of fasting and prayer. According to the Hebrew calendar, it is performed on the tenth day of the seventh month.